The Hut in the Old Tree

Story by Dawn McMillan

Illustrations by Meredith Thomas

In the school holidays,
Tess and Nathan always stayed
with their grandmother.
They loved making huts
at her place.

They made huts in the empty shed.
They made huts in the garden.
And they made huts
in secret places under the trees.

3

"Look, Nathan!" cried Tess.
"I've found a tunnel
under this old tree.
I can crawl right through
to the other side."

"Great!" said Nathan.
"We can build a good hut
in there."

Nathan and Tess found sticks
for the hut walls.
They put leaves on the hut floor.

Tess found a box in the shed.
"This box will be a great door,"
she said.

Tess and Nathan played in their hut
all afternoon.

"We'll play here again tomorrow,"
said Nathan,
as he pulled the door shut
behind him.

The next morning, Tess and Nathan
ran out to play in their hut.
Some of the sticks
were lying on the ground.

"Look at our hut!" cried Nathan.
"It's broken!"

"We can fix it," said Tess.

But the next day,
the hut was broken again.
Tess and Nathan were upset.

"Who is doing this?" said Nathan.

"Let's tell Gran about it," said Tess.

Gran came to look at the hut.

"Oh, dear," said Gran.
"I wonder if Danny
has been playing in your hut.
Look! Here he comes now!
He lives down the road.
He has no one to play with."

"Hey, Danny," called Nathan.
"Did you break our hut?"

Danny didn't say anything.
He looked down at the ground
and just kept on walking.

Nathan and Tess fixed their hut again.
They played in it for most of the day.
Then Tess said,
"If we are very quiet,
Danny could come back."

"Yes," said Nathan.
"Then we can catch him
if he tries to break our hut again."

Nathan and Tess sat very quietly
in their hut.
Soon they heard a noise.
Someone was pulling
the box away!

13

A boy crawled into the hut.
It was Danny!

"We knew it was you!" cried Tess.
"You **have** been breaking our hut!"

"I'm sorry," said Danny.
"I only wanted to play in it."

Tess looked at Danny.
"If you don't break our hut again,
then you can be our friend," she said.

"And you can play in here
with us, too," said Nathan.

"Hey, thanks," said Danny.
"I'll look after it for you,
when you go home."